What Else Can I Play
Violin
Grade Two

© International Music Publications Ltd
First published in 1996 by International Music Publications Ltd
International Music Publications Ltd is a Faber Music company
3 Queen Square, London WC1N 3AU
Series Editor: Mark Mumford
Cover designed by Lydia Merrills-Ashcroft
Music arranged and processed by Barnes Music Engraving Ltd
Printed in England by Caligraving Ltd
All rights reserved

ISBN10: 0-571-53061-3
EAN13: 978-0-571-53061-8

To buy Faber Music publications or to find out about the full range of titles available,
please contact your local music retailer or Faber Music sales enquiries:

Faber Music Ltd, Burnt Mill, Elizabeth Way, Harlow, CM20 2HX England
Tel: +44(0)1279 82 89 82   Fax: +44(0)1279 82 89 83
sales@fabermusic.com   fabermusic.com

Introduction

In this *What Else Can I Play?* collection you'll find sixteen popular tunes that are both challenging and entertaining.

The pieces have been carefully selected and arranged to create ideal supplementary material for young violinists who are either working towards or have recently taken a Grade Two violin examination.

As the student progresses through the volume, technical demands increase and new concepts are introduced which reflect the requirements of the major Examination Boards. Suggestions and guidelines on bowing, fingering, dynamics and tempo are given for each piece, together with technical tips and performance notes.

Pupils will experience a wide variety of music, ranging from folk and classical through to showtunes and popular songs, leading to a greater awareness of musical styles.

Whether it's for light relief from examination preparation, or to reinforce the understanding of new concepts, this collection will enthuse and encourage all young violin players.

What shall we do with the drunken sailor?

Traditional

The wraggle-taggle gypsies

Traditional

This is my lovely day

Words by Alan Patrick Herbert, Music by Vivian Ellis CBE

rit.

Do-re-mi

Words by Oscar Hammerstein II, Music by Richard Rodgers

The white cliffs of Dover

Words by Nat Burton, Music by Walter Kent

Prelude

Frédéric Chopin

Cavatina

Stanley Myers

Rudolph the red-nosed reindeer

Words and Music by Johnny Marks

My own true love
(Tara's theme)

Words and Music by Mack David and Max Steiner

Plaisir d'amour
(The smile of love)

Giovanni Martini

Santa Claus is comin' to town

Words by Haven Gillespie, Music by J Fred Coots

Don't sit under the apple tree
(with anyone else but me)

Words and Music by Lew Brown, Charles Tobias and Sam Stept

The man on the flying trapeze

George Leybourne and Alfred Lee

Holiday for strings

David Rose

Sing a rainbow

Words and Music by Arthur Hamilton

Autumn leaves
(Les Feuilles Mortes)

English words by Johnny Mercer, French words by Jacques Prévert, Music by Joseph Kosma